Piano Dreams
Solo pieces for piano

Book 1
by Anne Terzibaschitsch

Published by
Trinity College London Press
www.trinitycollege.com

Registered in England
Company no. 09726123

Copyright © 2016 Trinity College London Press
First impression, March 2016

Printed in England by Caligraving Ltd.
Music origination by Camden Music Services.
Illustrations by Ruth Keating.

Preface

One of the reasons I started writing pieces for piano lessons was that I wanted to provide material to help overcome specific musical and technical problems. I use the pieces to supplement standard piano tutor books; they are not intended to replace them.

Thankfully, a good selection of piano tutor books are available and even advanced pupils have ready access to a wide range of works for the piano. It is more difficult, however, to find suitable music for 'advanced beginners' at the intermediate level. One of the key things I like to focus on in my teaching is trying to eliminate and avoid the build-up of stiffness or tension while playing the piano. Since the sound of the piano is created by motion, it is very important to develop a harmonious, flowing action in order to shape the sound. The pieces are designed to promote freedom of movement through the demands of varying techniques and to familiarise pupils with different types of movement. Movement and life always go hand in hand, especially when you are trying to teach pupils to give vivid expression to the music they are creating.

The explanatory notes on each of the pieces provide suggestions on certain aspects of the pieces and how they might be approached, but they are by no means exhaustive.

At the request of some of my pupils I have added my own words to a number of the pieces; they have found them helpful in developing their feeling for the music and rhythm.

I hope that some of these pieces will be of use to my fellow piano teachers in their own lessons.

Anne Terzibaschitsch
Karlsruhe 1995

Contents

Notes

In **Evening Bell** (p5), a fifth played by the left hand brings out the bell motif. Using the pedal helps to reinforce the sonorous sound of the bell.

Lullaby (p6) spans a fifth in both hands. As pupils may not yet have learned to pass the thumb under the fingers, they should focus on the clarity of articulation in the right hand. The *legato* motif in the left hand conjures up the image of a rocking cradle.

In **Climbing Mountains** (p7) the steep ascent of the mountains is depicted by the use of the notes of the A natural minor scale. The left hand line can be interpreted as a steady stride. The pupil should strive for a firm touch.

It isn't necessary to lift the pedal in **Mountain Echo** (p8). The call and the echo can sound together.

Winter (p8) is intentionally written in D minor. Listen to how the music paints a bleak picture of winter.

The ability to play scales is required in **Evening Star** (p9). The left hand plays a span of just a fifth so the pupil can focus on the technical challenge in the right hand of passing the fingers and thumb over and under one another.

In **Little Waltz** (p10), two bars with a dotted rhythm are followed by two bars without dotted notes. This piece can be used to practise the combination of simultaneous rhythms.

The crotchets in the bass line portray the ever-circling (**The**) **Wheel of Fortune** (p11). The 'path of destiny' is represented by the tune in the right hand.

Interval Magic (p12) can be used as an exercise to introduce the idea of varying left hand intervals. It helps to familiarise pupils with intervals including the second, third, fourth and fifth.

Granny's Waltz (p13) is a lively, dance-like (waltz) piece. The rhythmic emphasis is on the first beat of the bar. The second and third crotchets in the left hand need a light touch.

The Little Donkey (p14) should be very popular with younger pupils. The right hand shapes the melody and at the same time tells a story (if you use your imagination), while the accompaniment paints a picture of the grey donkey trotting along.

Autumn (p15) provides practice in the conscious release of the left hand on the rests as the quavers are picked up in the right hand.

The difficulty in **Minuet** (p16) lies in articulating the notes exactly as they are written. The *staccato* on the upbeats and the final cadences should always be played with a free wrist.

Russian Song (p17) provides an opportunity to learn about syncopation. Speaking or singing the accompanying words helps to reinforce the rhythm of the music. The left hand can tap the beat or play the bass part.

The urge to get up and go comes through in **Happy Journey** (p18). A little trill exercise for the left hand begins in bar 9.

Pedal should be used throughout to play **Over the Water** (p19), but should be changed at each LH chord shift. This piece provides an opportunity to explain the term 'triplet' and gives a good illustration of the concept of phrasing.

The effect of **Sad Song** (p20) is created by the interplay of opposing forces. Listen to how the changing chord-shapes and continuously varying dynamics create the mood of the piece.

Each of the polyphonic (imitation) entries in **Shadow Pictures** (p21) should be brought out so that they are clearly audible. The teacher can use this piece to introduce the pupil to the style of J S Bach Inventions.

Hobby Horse (p22) is a *staccato* study. The main accents are always on the first and fourth quaver of each bar.

Steppes (p23) creates a picture in the mind's eye of the endless expanse of the landscape. What makes this piece difficult is smooth shaping of the transition in dynamic from *pianissimo* to *fortissimo* and back to *pianissimo* again.

The two themes representing two very different characters confront each other in **Two Characters** (p24). It might be helpful to get the pupil to start by describing the two characters in words before they try and interpret their musical counterparts.

Flying a Kite (p26) is a tricky exercise in fluency for the right hand.

At the Fair (p28) is a short character piece reflecting the lively, cheerful atmosphere of the fair.

The pensive character of **In Thought** (p29) is brought out by the minim in each bar of the bass line. The tempo should not be too fast.

The House Elves (p30) provides an opportunity to develop wrist flexibility as well as firm fingertips through playing the one- and two-note *staccato* figures.

In **The First Day at School** (p32), the pupil is introduced to each of the intervals, from the second to the octave, providing an opportunity for pupils to learn to adjust their left hand to different spans.

Notes (cont.)

A **Trip to Scotland** (p33) is written in three-part song form (ABA). In the B section, fifths in the bass line imitate bagpipes. Scotland is especially famous for its pipers and pipe bands.

The quick pace of **In a Hurry** (p34) helps to strengthen players' feeling for the beat and rhythm in music. This piece also puts the nimbleness of the right hand to the test.

Night Ride (p35) is in a minor key; listen to the mood it creates. The regular, rhythmic intervals in the left hand should be played from the wrist with a light bouncing action.

Rocks in the Stream (p36) combines both polyphonic and homophonic writing. The 'rocks' the water flows around are represented by the repeated F in the second section.

For Fast Fingers (p37) provides a useful warm up exercise for younger players as the repeated notes help to loosen up the wrist and the scales to develop agility.

Past Memories (p38) teaches the left hand to travel across the leaps in a controlled fashion. The right hand has to convey the character of the piece. The 'A' section represents the present and is in A minor. The 'B' section begins in a major key as it looks back on happy past times.

In **Dance of the Goblins** (p39), the left hand jumps must be quick and efficient. This is a good exercise for achieving accuracy.

In **Freedom** (p40), the crossing of the hands and moving confidently into a different position help to develop a strong sense of keyboard geography.

In **Gypsy Tune** (p41), both hands play syncopated rhythms, which adds to the difficulty of this piece. Pupils could try to imitate the sound of a guitar with their left hand.

A **Ballet Lesson** (p42) should be played with controlled arm weight, allowing each of the dynamics to sound clearly. Care should be taken to ensure that the touch is even when playing the 'pirouettes' (bars 9-11).

Arietta (p43) means 'little aria'. The main notes of the melody need to sing out clearly above the accompaniment.

The pupil should try to bring out the melody clearly in **Christmas** (p44).

Evening Bell

Moderato

Hear how the church bell's sil - ver - y sound,

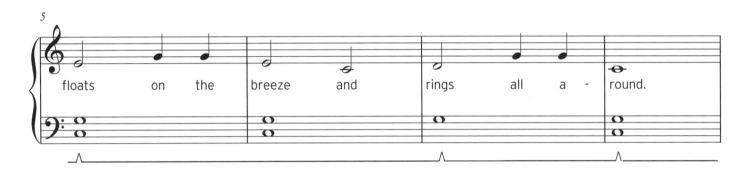

floats on the breeze and rings all a - round.

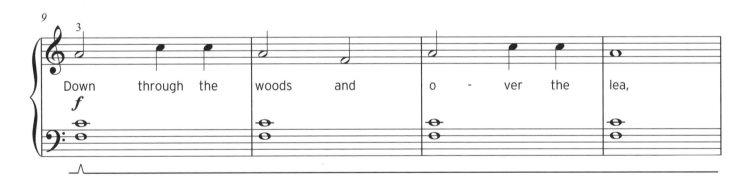

Down through the woods and o - ver the lea,

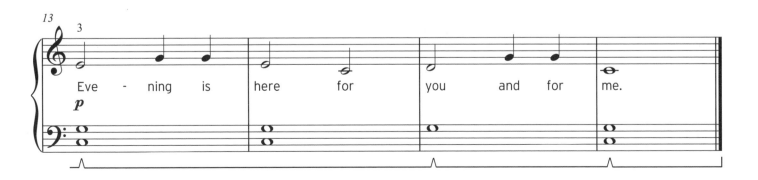

Eve - ning is here for you and for me.

Lullaby

Ba - by sweet, soft - ly sleep, dream sweet dreams and__ slum - ber.

Stars on high in the sky, who can tell their__ num - ber?

Climbing Mountains

Slowly

Mountain Echo

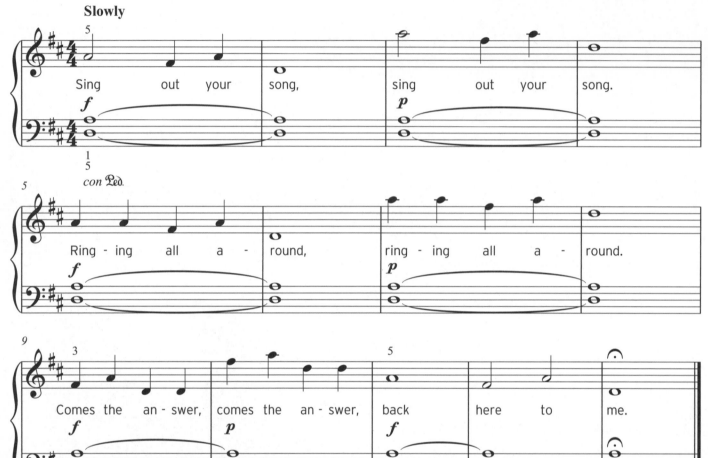

Winter

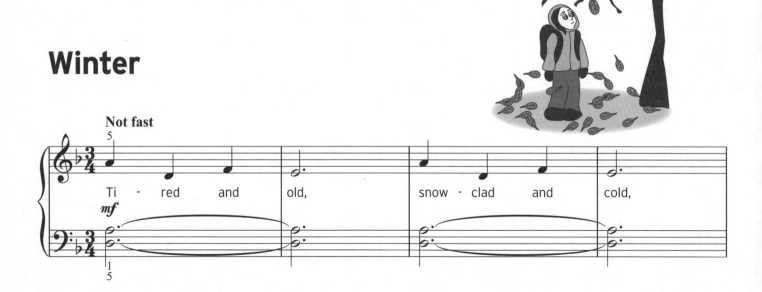

frozen they shiver in winter's cruel hold. All bare and brown,

si-lent they frown, hum-bly they stand with their crowns hang-ing down.

rit.

Evening Star

Calmly

Look at that glit-ter-ing star on high, Twink-ling o-ver towns and lands a-far.

mf

Each day it tells us that night is___ nigh, That's___ why it's called the Eve-ning___ Star.

Little Waltz

The Wheel of Fortune

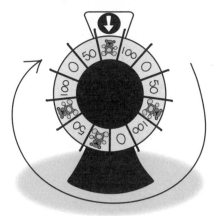

On and on the wheel goes round, day
by day, Where the path leads,
up or down, who can say?

Interval Magic

Andante

Can you hear them sing - ing, three notes bright-ly ring - ing?

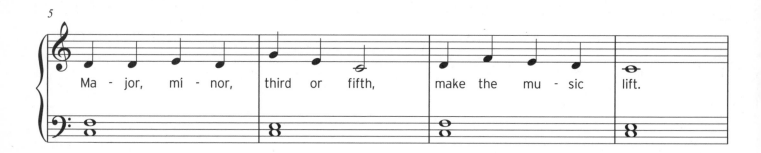

Ma - jor, mi - nor, third or fifth, make the mu - sic lift.

Now to - ge - ther play - ing, no - tice what they're say - ing!

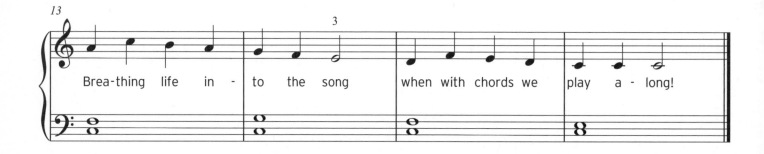

Brea-thing life in - to the song when with chords we play a - long!

Granny's Waltz

Allegretto

The Little Donkey

Autumn

Minuet

Russian Song

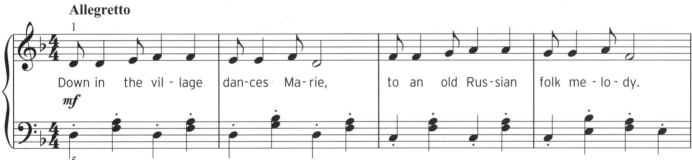

Allegretto

Down in the vil-lage dan-ces Ma-rie, to an old Rus-sian folk me-lo-dy.

Arms out, spin round and sway, to the fidd-ler's play - ing.

Cast all your cares a-way, that's what the mu-sic's say - ing.

Happy Journey

Over the Water

Sad Song

Shadow Pictures

Hobby Horse

Steppes

Two Characters

Reconciliation

Flying a Kite

Copyright © 1995 by Musikverlag Holzschuh, Manching
English version printed under licence by Trinity College London Press

At the Fair

In Thought

Andante

The House Elves

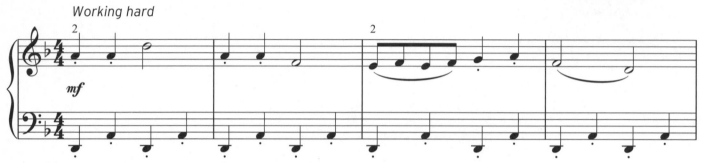

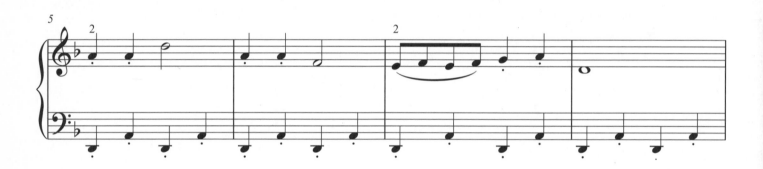

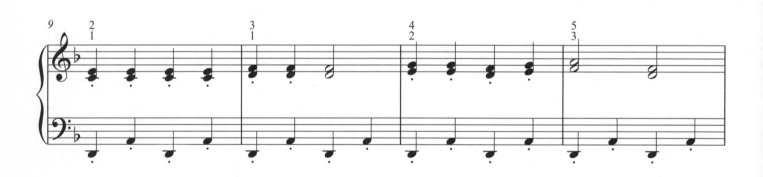

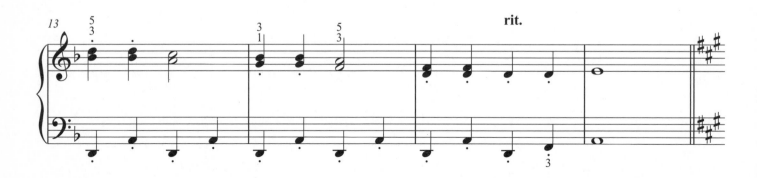

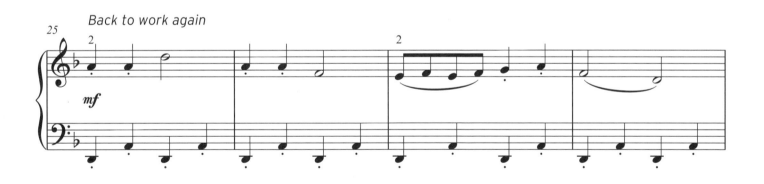

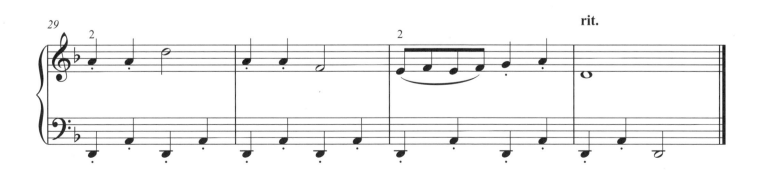

The First Day at School

A Trip to Scotland

In a Hurry

Night Ride

Rocks in the Stream

For Fast Fingers

Past Memories

Dance of the Goblins

Freedom

Gypsy Tune

Rhythmically

A Ballet Lesson

Arietta

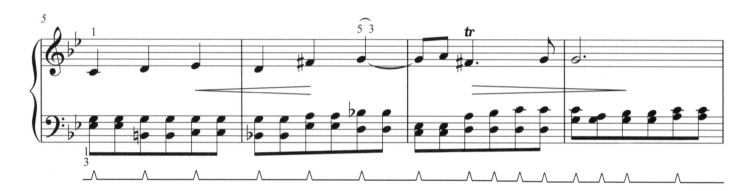

Christmas

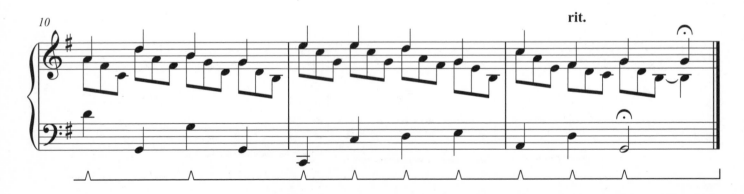